The Train of Fe

GW00809199

Story written by Adrian Bradbury

Illustrated by Kim Barnes

How to help your child read this book

This book gives your child extra practice in reading a story that includes sounds he or she has learnt at school.

Ask your child to read the Story Green Words and Red Words below, before reading the story. Do not read the story to your child first. Point to the words as he or she reads. If your child hesitates, help him or her to sound-blend the word.

Re-read each sentence or page to keep the plot moving. Children's attention is focused on reading the words and they find it hard to focus on the story at the same time.

Don't make them struggle too much and praise them when they succeed. Do it all with patience and love!

Story Green Words
Story Green Words are made up of sounds your child has already learnt. This book contains the following green words:

lur ched   spooky   against   ear-splitting

soo thingly   dangling   scaredy-cats   pleaded

Red Words
Red Words are harder to read because the letters represent unusual sounds. Ask your child to read the red words, but if he or she gets stuck on a word, read the word to your child. This book contains the following red words:

all   oth er   were   wanted

through   th eir   could

Important note

Read stories to your children that are beyond the level they can read for themselves – every evening. They'll only want to become readers if they experience the joy of listening to a range of stories, non-fiction and poetry. Very soon, they will be able to read those books for themselves, as well as listen to them.

Vocabulary check

Tell your child the meaning of each word in the context of the story.

	definition:	sentence:
lurched	moved suddenly and unsteadily	The train lurched forwards …
pitch darkness	completely black, with no light	… through the doors into pitch darkness.
wispy	fine and feathery	Wispy things, like cobwebs, brushed against our faces.
ear-splitting	extremely loud	Then Mum let out an ear-splitting scream …
soothingly	said calmly to comfort someone	"Don't be scared, Mum," said Deb soothingly.
dangling	hanging or swinging loosely	It's just a model dangling from wires.
tiresome	when someone makes you feel bored or annoyed	But that was nothing compared to the sounds our tiresome parents were making.
burbling	making continuous and confusing sounds	We spent the entire ride with the pair of them whimpering, burbling and moaning behind us.

Last Friday, we all went to the funfair. All night long, Deb and I tried to get our mum and dad to take us on the Train of Fear. They just kept making excuses and took us on other rides instead. Then they claimed they were tired and wanted to go home.

The Train of Fear

Deb was fed up and cross.

"You can't go to the funfair without going on the Train of Fear!" she complained. "It's just not right!"

In the end, Mum and Dad realised it was hopeless and gave in.

Dad enquired about a family ticket. Soon, we were strapped into our seats, ready to go. The train lurched forwards, through the doors into pitch darkness.

Spooky tunes filled the air. Wispy things, like cobwebs, brushed against our faces. Then Mum let out an ear-splitting scream as a vampire suddenly appeared in front of us.

"Look at those fangs!" she screamed.

"Don't be scared, Mum," said Deb soothingly. "It's not real. It's just a model dangling from wires." Deb fears nothing.

Skeletons were soon dancing around us, glowing in the darkness.

Monsters with bulging eyes lumbered up to us. We could hear howling, screeching and wailing sounds all around.

But that was nothing compared to the sounds our tiresome parents were making. We spent the entire ride with the pair of them whimpering, burbling and moaning behind us.

By the time the ride ended, Mum's face was as white as a sheet. Dad looked as if he was ready to faint.

"So that's why you didn't want to go on the Train of Fear!" Deb chuckled. "You're a pair of scaredy-cats!"

"Yes, dear, you're right," gasped Mum.

"Can we go home now?" pleaded Dad.

Questions to read and answer

Ask your child to read the questions and answer them without your help.

1. Why did Mum and Dad give in to the children's demands?

2. Why do you think Mum and Dad sat behind their children?

3. As well as the dangling models, what else would have made Mum and Dad scared?

4. What did Mum and Dad want to do after the Train of Fear? Why?

Retell the story

Take turns retelling the story with your child.

14